Ready to Read

Hay for Ambrosia

by Jane Buxton

KT-460-994

photographs by Lynnley Driver

2100133554

E.L.R.S.

631.49(E)

REFERENCE

2100003190

It is hot and sunny —
good weather for making hay.

The grass is cut with a big mower.
It dries in the sun and the wind.

The hay rake turns the grass over
to dry the other side.

The baler gathers up the rows of dried grass.

It presses the grass together
and ties it up with string.

The bales come out of the chute,
and we haul them to the barn.

In the winter,
when the grass doesn't grow,
Ambrosia will have hay to eat.

Ways of Storing Hay

Under plastic

In barns